Never Play Snap With a Shark

John Foster is Britain's most p... having compiled over a hundred anthologies of children's poetry. He divides his time between writing, running workshops and giving performances to children. He is married, with two children and two grandchildren called Evie and Louis. He lives in Oxfordshire and his hobbies are gardening, skiing and supporting Carlisle United.

Sally Kindberg is an illustrator and writer. Her children's books include *Robotina Finds Out* and *Creepy Kokey*. She has worked for the *Independent*, the *Guardian* and the BBC. She loves travelling and writing about it, and her trips have included sailing in a Tall Ships race, and going to Elf School in Iceland. She lives with robots and wind-up toys, and has a daughter called Emerald.

Never Play Snap With a Shark

Chosen by John Foster

Illustrated by Sally Kindberg

MACMILLAN CHILDREN'S BOOKS

First published 2001 by Macmillan Children's Books
This edition produced 2001 for
The Book People Ltd,
Hall Wood Avenue,
Haydock, St Helens WA11 9UL

ISBN 0 330 39370 7

3 5 7 9 8 6 4

A CIP catalogue record for this book is available from the British Library.

Printed by Mackays of Chatham plc, Chatham, Kent.

'Dirty Gertie Mackintosh' by Dick King-Smith is reproduced by permission of
A. P. Watt Ltd on behalf of Fox Busters Ltd.
'The Cupboard on the Landing' by John Coldwell first published in
Never Say Boo to a Ghost by OUP 1990.
'A Cautionary Tale' by Pat Moon first published in *Earthlives* by Pimlico 1991.© Pat Moon 1991.
'The Zombie Horror' by Gareth Owen from *Collected Poems for Children* by Gareth Owen
by Macmillan 2000.
'Miss Eva Garibaldi' by Coral Rumble first published in *Baboons' Bottoms* by Initiative Press 1995.

Contents

Sandra Slater

Here lies what's left of Sandra Slater
Who poked her pet — an alligator —
Forgetting that to tease or bait her
Might annoy an alligator.

Alas, the alligator ate her.

John Foster

hic!

Never Play Rugby with a Dinner Lady

Never play rugby with a dinner lady
Never juggle with a porcupine
Never have a bath with an alligator
Never make faces at Frankenstein.

Never put piranhas on the toilet seat
Never burp in a silent test
Never sleep facedown on a bed of nails
Never go to school in Great-Granny's vest.

Never play cards with an octopus
Never play snap with a shark
Never keep ferrets in your underwear
Never make fun of a Doberman's bark.

Never make shoes for a millipede
Never milk a cow when it's a bull
Never try to find a rhyme for silver
Never talk to wolves when the moon is full.

Never stick your tongue out at teachers
Never ignore your mummy's curse
Never play frisbee with Dad's records
Always listen to cautionary verse.

Paul Cookson

The Cupboard on the Landing

Mary had been told
Never to wipe her nose on her skirt,
Never to run in the house,
And
Never never to open the cupboard on the landing.

But one day,
After blowing her nose on a clean handkerchief,
She walked up the stairs,
Intent upon opening the cupboard on the landing.

First she
Turned the key in the lock,
Then she turned the other key in the other lock,
Slid back the top bolt,
The bottom bolt
And the six bolts in between.
Then she cut through the chains,
Removed the barbed wire,
Switched off the alarm,
Threw her handkerchief over the video camera,
Undid the combination
And opened the cupboard door.

And what did Mary see
In the cupboard on the landing?
Nothing.
But
Something in the cupboard on the landing saw Mary.
And Mary was never seen again.

John Coldwell

Surfing the Weird Wild Web

We bought Tom a computer
We thought that it was right
And he sat and surfed the Internet
Till deep into the night
And he came across a website
In a dark and dismal hue
With an ancient voice that whispered
'I've been waiting . . . just for you.
Now if you'll give some details
Click on the form, that's right
Just name, address, and blood group
And where you sleep at night.
Then E-mail me a photo
Not some great big cheesy grin
But a close-up of the region
From your shoulders to your chin.
Now send it to me straight away
While you're still young and fresh
And I'll drop in one evening
To meet you in the flesh.'
Now since he found this website
Tom's gone through such a change
I'd never thought the Internet
Could make a lad so strange.
His skin has gone so pallid
His features are so drawn
He prowls the house the whole night long
And goes to bed at dawn.
So I searched, and found the website
Now I know where he logged in
And I smashed up the computer
And I threw it in the bin.

I searched and found the website
Please don't let your children go
To www.dracula.co—

Paul Bright

7

A Warning

Paul's mother warned, on Guy Fawkes day,
'Remember to keep well away
from fireworks or you may learn
that they can give a nasty burn.'
'Mother dear, you're always right,'
he sneered, and later on that night
he left the house, his hands and pockets
filled with bangers, squibs and rockets.
He'd arranged to meet his mates
outside the park, beside the gates.
Ignoring each and every mother,
they threw their bangers at each other.
Paul pushed his rockets in his belt
and as the bangers flew, he felt
a sputter as a fuse ignited.

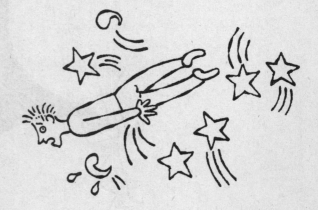

The other boys stepped back, delighted,
uttering cries of 'Ooh' and 'Aah'
as Paul became a rising star
spraying sparks of red and blue
as up into the air he flew.
His shoes smoked faintly on the ground.
His shoes were all they ever found.

Marian Swinger

9

A Cautionary Tale

Little Pete would only eat
Packaged puddings very sweet,
Fizzy drinks with tartrazine,
Pork pies and pastries filled with cream.
He ignored his parents' desperate pleas
To eat vegetables, or fruit or cheese,
For his craving for E2s tabooed
Any sort of healthy food.
Then they noticed with alarm
His legs had started to embalm.
As the process reached his chin,
Still little Pete would not give in,
And to the end his cry was 'Never!'
Now little Pete's preserved for ever.
They keep him propped up in the hall
As a warning to you all,
Not to share their young son's fate,
Who perished before his sell-by date.

Pat Moon

Square Eyed James

This is the tale of Square Eyed James
Who liked to play computer games.
So what? you cry, That's not a crime –
Unless you do it all the time.

But that is just what James would do.
He'd play each night, till one or two.
He'd snatch a nap from two till four
Then climb from bed and play some more.

When all his friends went to the park,
He'd sit alone in dismal dark,
His eyes directed at the screen.
Believe you me, that boy was keen.

They tried to tempt him from his chair
With talk of sun and good, fresh air.
But still young James just stared and sat.
The kid was hooked, and that was that.

But staring at a screen's unwise.
In time, it can affect your eyes.
One day, he got a nasty scare.
His mum said, James! Your eyes are square!

Just look into this mirror, lad!
He did. They were. Now, this was bad!
In vain he wept and cried, Unfair!
His eyes were well and truly square.

Now, people point and call him names,
Despite dark glasses with huge frames.
So, kids. Beware computer games!
Do not end up like Square Eyed James.

Kaye Umansky

13

The Tale of Penelope Knox

This is the tale of Penelope Knox,
A girl completely addicted to chocs.
From dawn to dusk she'd greedily munch
Chocolate, for breakfast, dinner and lunch.

Her friends all said, 'Give up this lust
And just drink cocoa, if you must,'
But Penny laughed and ate more bars
Of Kit-Kat, Yorkies and king-size Mars.

Mum said, 'Penny's ways I can't condone
She'll finish her life on her Tobler-own.'
But sadly one day this chocoholic
Suffered a bout of cocoa colic.

Her skin turned brown (the milky sort)
Although against the colic she fought.
She said, 'I know life's door is nearly shut,
But just one more square of Fruit and Nut.'

They wrapped her up in silver foil,
And dug the chocolate-coloured soil.
Then said 'Farewell, dear Penny Chocs',
And lowered the life-sized Dairy Box.

Her end, the chocoholic's fate,
Was living beyond her sell-by date.
The family said, 'We're so glad that she
Asked to be buried near Cadbury.'

David Whitehead

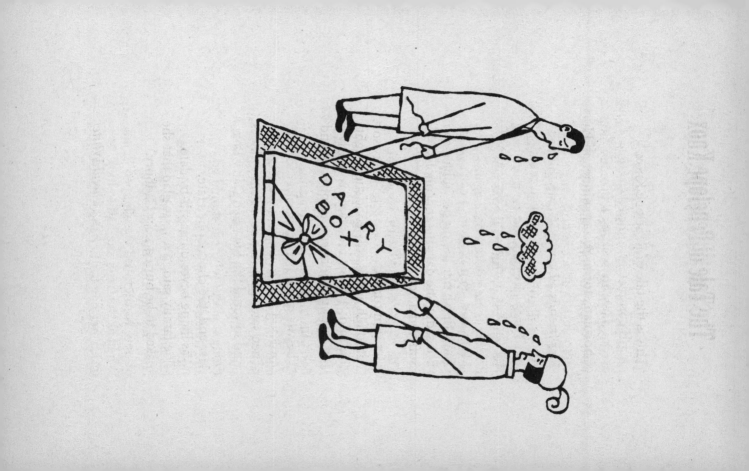

Sprocket's Pockets

Thomas Joseph Samuel Sprocket
filled each and every trouser pocket,
until conveniently stuffed
with sweets and toffee (lightly fluffed),
catapults of rubber bands,
treasure maps (complete with sand),
string and conkers, gun-shaped sticks,
paper clips and Lego bricks.
His mum said, 'Tom! I'll go insane,
if I sort these pockets once again –
next time I need to wash your gear,
I want to find your pockets clear!
Last week your socks and pants went green
with felt tip ink, in the machine.
The filter's clogged with tissues you
have left inside your pockets too –
and you should hear the dreadful din
your marbles make caught in the spin.
Now listen, Tom, I'll make this plain –
don't fill these pockets up again,
go empty out this little lot
and put them in their PROPER SPOT!'
So Thomas, to his mother's pleasure,
sadly emptied out his treasure,
thought about where it should go,
and tidied it away just so –
then quickly walked to school before
his mum could ask him any more.
Now this explains the sorry tale
of how Tom's mum was clapped in jail.
When at the bank she had to look
inside her bag for her chequebook.

16

She heaved it on the side and had
a search through keys and pen and pad –
then found something to make her mad!
There with her cards and wrinkle cream,
and specs and tissues (used and clean),
there was a Lego submarine.

17

Beneath her purse and spare black tights
and torch for 'walkies' on dark nights,
a sight that made her lips go white –
her bills and vouchers had become
stuck fast with toffee, every one!
(She had to suck some off her thumb.)
Worse, make-up, mirror, powder puff,
eyeshadow and eyelash stuff,
all hairy with Tom's pocket fluff!
Between the photo of her son
and pack of mints to soothe her tum,
she pulled an automatic gun!
She growled out loud and waved the toy,
and hissed, 'I'm going to kill that boy!'
The cashier screamed (a nasty sound),
everyone crashed to the ground,
and Tom's mum, aghast and pale,
was captured, handcuffed, sent to jail.

Poor Tom was left home on his own –
and used the wash machine alone –
ignored the clank, the grind, the smoke,
and other hints that it was broke –
till it thrashed free with a mad roar
and bounced and sloshed across the floor,
squashed Tom, who stood there unaware
quite flat inside his underwear.
The last words gasped by Thomas Sprocket –
'If I had only cleared my pockets!'

Liz Brownlee

Up in Smoke

Cornelius loved Chemistry
It had a strange attraction
The final words he spoke were 'Sir?
Is this a chain reaction?'

Paul Bright

Epitaph to a Victim of Designer Fashion

A warning, in memory of Annabel Hayling,
Whose designer laces were designed to be trailing.
When tied in a bow, as young Annabel said,
The expensive wording just couldn't be read.
Her parents pleaded that Annabel tie them,
But Annabel, foolishly, chose to defy them.
To all who, like her, might disregard warnings
In favour of fashion on dark winter mornings,
Beware of steep stairways and designer crazes,
Remember poor Annabel. DO UP YOUR LACES!

Daphne Kitching

Miss Eva Garibaldi

a cautionary tale

Miss Eva Garibaldi
Was a teacher of some years,
Whose career was punctuated
By her breaking down in tears.
The children rarely listened
To the lessons she'd prepared,
But chose to play a game or two,
Usually in pairs.

Miss Eva Garibaldi
Was a 'Miss', make no mistake,
She lived alone in Eastbourne,
Where she would very rarely break
The habits of her solitude,
Meticulously planned,
And where she played the tuba
In the local big brass band.

Miss Eva Garibaldi
Had patiently restrained
Her hand from making contact
With a bottom, and she'd tamed
A volatile volcano of
A temper that once drowned
The foghorn from the cliff top
Of her dearly loved home town.

Miss Eva Garibaldi
Was misjudged as weak and shy,
The tears she'd wept had hidden
Building anger in her eyes,
The children hadn't noticed
Curious changes in her mood,
And saw no reason to hold back
From being cruel and rude.

Miss Eva Garibaldi
Took the children on a trip,
(The sort you have to write about
When you've returned from it,)
She took them to a cliff top
So they could admire the view,
Then she lifted up her tuba
And blew and blew and blew.

Miss Eva Garibaldi
Watched the children jump in fear
Of the strange and piercing noises
That played havoc with their ears.
Then Miss Eva Garibaldi
Went to the Head to say
That her recent fear of teaching
Had been completely swept away.

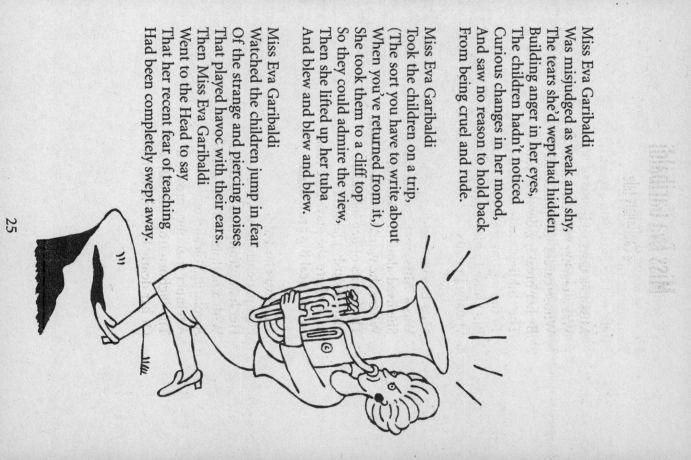

So if you call a teacher names
Or show some disrespect,
Remember their reaction
Might not be what you expect.
She may dissolve in floods of tears
And abandon work that's planned,
But she just might take you on a trip
With a tuba in her hand.

Coral Rumble

Catapult Crazy

Dudley's ninth birthday
Was when it began.
He had an ace present
From his loving gran.

The gift was amazing,
A catapult blue
With bright red elastic
And green ammo too!

Well, Dud was ecstatic.
When twanged it felt great.
There was just one problem.
He couldn't shoot straight!

He cracked next door's window,
He smashed Dad's best mug,
He bust his gran's Gameboy
And just gave a shrug.

He twanged the computer,
The screen shattered, POP!
He twanged Mum's best Ming vase.
His gran shouted, 'STOP!!!'

But Dudley kept twanging
As little boys will.
'I feel just like Dennis
The Menace – It's brill!!!!!'

He twanged at his hamster,
He twanged at his dad,
He twanged at the TV,
Made everyone mad!

He twanged at his teacher,
He twanged at his friends,
He twanged at the neighbours,
But that's where it ends.

'Cos Gran got so fed up
Of Dud, she saw red,
And tying elastic
'Tween garage and shed

She lifted her grandson
And holding him tight,
She twanged him straight up.
Britain's new satellite!

Last seen he was floating
With dread on his face,
Being twanged at by comets.
A target in space.

So if you behave like
A Beano cartoon,
You too might become the
Next Man in the Moon!

Rachael House

Cautionary Epitaphs

Here lies the body
Of superior Clare:
Tripped over the kerb
With her head in the air.

Here lies the body
Of careless, young Kate:
Took no note of the sign
'Beware Bull!' on the gate.

Here lies the body
Of thoughtless, young John.
He tried to feed chips
To an angry, old swan.

Here lies the body
Of Valerie Jean:
Ignored firework warnings
Last year's Hallowe'en.

Here lie the remains
Of Cousin Louise.
She went for a swim
In the shark-filled South Seas.

Here lies the body
Of little George Gold.
He never did learn
To do as he was told.

John Kitching

Some Grave Consequences of Visits to the Zoo

There was a boy called Henry Page,
who went into a lion's cage.
The lion cried, 'I do enjoy
a tasty little human boy.'
And though he'd only just been fed,
he promptly bit off Henry's head.

Jenny thought the bears looked sweet
and gave them her packed lunch to eat.
This was a foolish thing to do
because the bears ate Jenny, too.

32

The crocodile grinned from ear to ear
when sweet little Angela Jones went near.
'What a dear little child,'
the crocodile smiled.
And her smile grew even wider,
as Angela Jones disappeared inside her.

Kate said, 'If I stroke its fur,
I can make the tiger purr.'
But Kate was wrong – and that's because
she quite forgot its claws and jaws!

'Teacher, teacher, Jimmy Jakes
is playing with the poisonous snakes!'
Teacher said, with a secret smile,
'We won't disturb them for a while.'
And added, with a nasty smirk,
'Let's give the poison time to work!'

Cynthia Rider

Right Daft

When I'm playing the fool in the playground
The kids all come crowding round near;
When I'm chucking out jokes in the classroom
They snigger and chuckle and cheer;
When I'm acting right daft for the teachers
They're grinning from ear to ear;
So why, when it's ended in trouble,
Am I the only one here?

Penny Dolan

Little Miss Fidget

She fiddled with the stereo,
The washer and the phone.
Anything with dials on
Was in her fiddle zone.
But now her hands are bandaged up.
She's resting for a while.
She did not read the sign that said:
'Don't touch the croc-o-dial.'

Bill Condon

35

The Boy Who Boasted

John Bragger was born with a very big head:
it grew bigger and bigger with all that he said.

He boasted, 'I'm braver and better than you.'
He boasted so much that his face became blue,

and he almost arrived at a premature death
from boasting so much that he ran out of breath.

'I'm the fastest,' he boasted, 'at running in school,'
but everyone knew that he wasn't at all.

'I'm the quickest at sums,' he continued, 'I'm bright.'
(He was quickest, but none of his answers were right.)

'I'm loudest at singing.' (We won't deny that,
but he sang even worse than the caretaker's cat.)

At most things in school, in fact, John was the worst,
but his head grew so big that we thought it would burst.

He could only just manage to squeeze through the door:
we were sure that it couldn't increase any more,

but it did and we even began to feel sorry
when he had to be taken to school in a lorry.

He carried on boasting about his success:
'I'm the best playing football. I'm brilliant at chess.

'I'm dead good at music. I've made a CD.
They've said I can have my own show on TV.'

'I'm so rich that I'll soon be a billionaire,'
At times passers-by used to stop and stare,

for he couldn't fit now into classrooms at all
and a crane had to lower him into the hall.

His brain was no bigger, I'd say, than a prune
but his head was the size of a hot-air balloon.

We thought it might happen, and it did so one day –
he boasted so much that he floated away.

He got smaller and smaller and higher and higher,
still boasting away (what a terrible liar):

'My computer's the biggest that anyone's seen.
Did I tell you last week I had tea with the Queen?

'Once I rowed in a boat down Niagara Falls.
My dad is a film star. My mum's won the pools.

'The American president told me next June
I can go in a rocket and visit the moon.'

With hardly a pause he continued to boast
as he soared over London and then to the coast,

but where he is now it seems nobody knows –
I suppose it depends on the way the wind blows.

(So maybe one day if you look up you'll spy
a huge head with legs drifting high in the sky.)

Our teacher pronounced, 'It's a bit of a mess,'
and various stories appeared in the press.

37

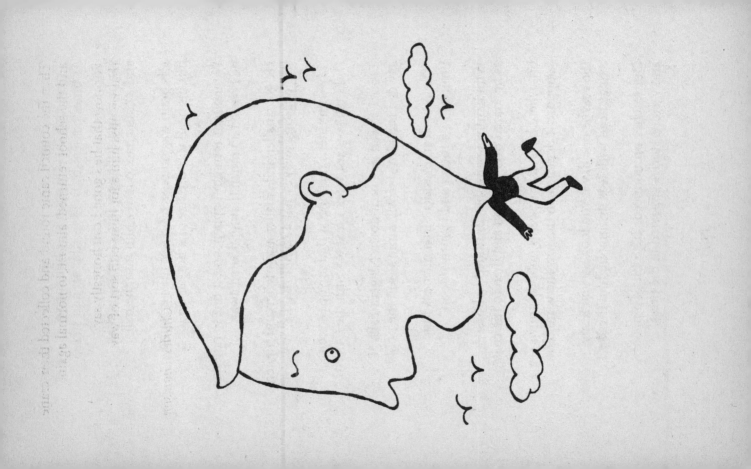

Then the council came round and collected their crane
and the school returned, almost, to normal again.

For now that he's gone I can honestly say
that we miss him a lot in an odd sort of way.

Charles Thomson

The Chilling Story of Archibald West

There was a boy called Archie West
who always thought that he knew best.
In fact, young Archie really thought
he was too clever to be taught.

He took no notice of his mother,
his father, sister, or his brother,
and never took their good advice,
for which he paid a heavy price.

For one cold morning, Mrs West
told Archie he must wear his vest.
She pointed out that chilly breezes
often lead to coughs and sneezes.

But Archie said, 'Vests are not cool.
I will not wear a vest to school,
for even if there is a storm,
I know that I'll be really warm.'

A cruel North wind blew that day
and when they all went out to play,
the other children's cheeks were rosy
because their vests were warm and cosy.

But Archie had no vest at all
and as the snow began to fall
his nose grew red, his fingers numb,
and he began to look quite glum.

'Oh, how I wish,' said Archie West.
'That I'd been wise and worn a vest.
If I had done as I was told,
I would not feel so very cold.'

And then he sniffed, and then he sneezed.
And then he coughed, and then he wheezed.
'Oh dear, oh dear,' said Archie West.
'I've caught a chill upon my chest.'

Worse was to come, for drifting snows
swirled all around poor Archie's toes.
His feet, his ankles, then his knees,
bit by bit, began to freeze.

His bottom, waist, and then his chest
(quite unprotected by a vest)
were frozen absolutely through,
and Archie turned completely blue.

Soon the freezing ice had spread
from his toes up to his head.
Icicles hung from his fingertips
and from his ears and nose and lips.

And by the time playtime was through
Archibald West was an ice statue.
Yes, he had turned to solid ice
because he would not take advice.

Cynthia Rider

41

Knotty Girl!

A young yoga fanatic called Lister
who was showing a trick to her sister
became stuck for a year
with her toe in her ear
till they managed, at last, to untwist her!

Colin Macfarlane

Francesca, who would not go to bed

There was a child, Francesca Flyte,
Who would not go to bed at night.
At nine p.m. her mother, Jane,
Would chant the following refrain,
'It's bedtime, Frankie, off you go.'

The girl would simply answer 'No!'

'You'll fall asleep again at school
Or halfway down the swimming pool.
One of these days, you'll be too weak
To run or walk or even speak!'

Alas Francesca did not hear
The warning of her mother dear.
'Don't treat me like a child of seven,
All my class stay up till eleven.'

One morning in the autumn gloom,
Francesca drooped into the room.
The circles round her eyes were black.

'Fantastic!' cried her brother Jack
Spilling the cornflakes he was eating,
'We'll make a fortune trick or treating.
One look at you will make 'em scream
When we go out on Hallowe'en.'

43

Francesca Flyte was horrified,
Ran to the mirror, shrieked and cried,
Then staggered back and clasped her mother,
'He's right, my horrid little brother,
I look almost as old as you,
Oh Mum, whatever shall I do?'

At eight o'clock now, every night,
Francesca Flyte puts out the light,
And snuggles down inside her bed
With Heffalump and Little Ted
(For even big girls love their toys)
And dreams of beating all the boys
At swimming, basketball and gym.
The circles round her eyes grow dim.

Poor Jack bewails, 'On Hallowe'en
My sis becomes a beauty queen!
I need someone who looks a fright –
I say, Mum, are you free tonight?'

'I have a date, I'll take my broom,
And you can tidy up your room.'

Petonelle Archer

The Zombie Horror

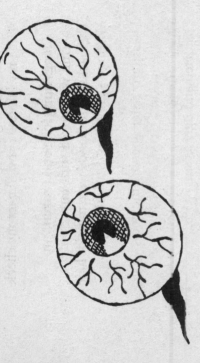

One dark and wintry evening
When snow swirled through the air
And the wind howled like a banshee
I crept silently up the stair.

I sat in the quiet of my bedroom
And opened with bated breath
My Zombie-Horror Make-Up Kit
That would frighten my sister to death.

FRIGHTEN YOUR FAMILY! AMAZE YOUR FRIENDS!
WITH OUR DO-IT-YOURSELF MAKE-UP KITS.
BE A WEREWOLF! A VAMPIRE! A ZOMBIE-GHOUL!
SCARE YOUR NEIGHBOURS OUT OF THEIR WITS!

Slowly my face began to change
As I carefully applied the pack.
I grinned at my face in the mirror
But an evil stranger leered back.

Long hair sprouted wild from my forehead,
My nose was half snout, half beak,
My right eye bulged angry and bloodshot
While my left one crawled over my cheek.

My fangs hung long and broken,
My chin was broken with sores,
The backs of my hands were mats of hair
My fingers grew long, bird-like claws.

I heard my sister opening the door,
Heard her call, 'Hello, anyone in?'
I took a long, last look at the thing in the glass
Distorted and ugly as sin.

My sister was running the water
I could hear her washing her hair.
I heard her call out as a floorboard creaked,
'Hello, is that somebody there?'

I released my zombie howl
As I crashed through the kitchen door,
Then I saw this ghoul in the window pane
And passed out cold on the floor.

Gareth Owen

Dirty Gertie Mackintosh

Dirty Gertie Mackintosh
Never had a proper wash.
'Wash your hands,' her mum would say
Six or seven times a day,
But she never would obey.

Gertie Mackintosh was bad,
For she would pretend she had.
'Washed your hands?' her mum would cry.
''Course I have,' she would reply
But it always was a lie.

Gertie simply couldn't stand
Using soap on either hand
Or her face. As well as those,
Gertie never blew her nose,
Never cleaned between her toes,

Never wrinkled out the wax
From her ears, nor washed their backs.
She would take a bath if told,
Lying there as good as gold
Till the water got too cold,

And she'd splash about and sing,
But she never washed a thing,
Not her body, nor her hair
Which was dark, though really fair.
She was dirty everywhere.

Soon, you possibly might think,
Gertie would begin to stink.
You'd be right. Before too long
Gertie gave out such a strong
And a penetrating pong

That it started to annoy
Every other girl and boy.
'Ugh! The smelly little fool!'
Cried the children at her school.
'Chuck her in the swimming pool!'

So, with a tremendous splosh,
In went Gertie Mackintosh.
As they watched her disappear
Underneath the waters clear,
Everybody gave a cheer.

'Swim!' they said. 'I can't!' she cried
To the children on the side
As she splashed about in vain.
Down she went and down again.
She was drowning, it was plain.

Someone watching gave a shout.
'Gertie! If we pull you out,
Will you promise you will be
Just as nice and clean as we
Are, for all eternity?'

'Yes!' gasped Gertie. 'Gurgle! Glug!'
So they gave her hair a tug,
Fished her from the waters green.
Never more was Gertie seen
To be otherwise than clean.

Dick King-Smith

Horrible Henry

Henry was hateful, spiteful, bad,
Teased the girls and made them mad.

Horrible Henry hated Harriet
(Popular, pretty, happy-as-Larry-et).

Henry tied poor Harriet's hair
(Two long plaits) to the back of her chair.

Stole her dinner-money, hid her shoes,
Locked her up inside the loos.

Henry boasted: 'My dad's rich.'
Harriet said, 'My aunt's a witch.'

Henry said, 'From what I've learnt
Ain't no witches. All got burnt.'

'Not my Auntie Dorothea,'
Harriet said, and went to see her.

Dorothea waved her wand.
Henry landed in a pond.

Green and slimy, hopping mad,
He sits upon a lily pad

Croaking loudly in Frogese
'Kiss me, Harriet! Kiss me, please!'

Pam Gidney

51

The TV Addict

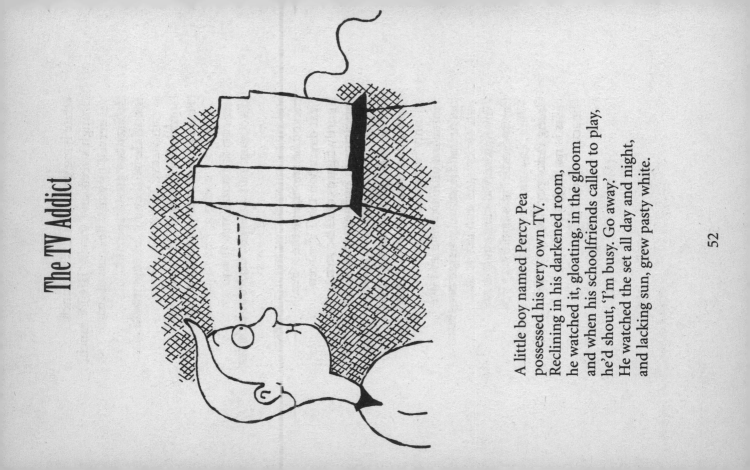

A little boy named Percy Pea
possessed his very own TV.
Reclining in his darkened room,
he watched it, gloating, in the gloom
and when his schoolfriends called to play,
he'd shout, 'I'm busy. Go away.'
He watched the set all day and night,
and lacking sun, grew pasty white.

While lying prone, he'd idly munch
through sweets and snacks. His TV lunch
was served upstairs. Because of that,
the lazy boy grew rather fat,
and while he chewed, his eyes would glaze
as radioactive TV rays
bombarded him and subtly changed
the way his atoms were arranged.
One stormy evening, Percy's luck
ran out; the aerial was struck.
His screams drowned by the thunder's din,
the television sucked him in
and when his mother brought him tea,
she found no sign of Percy Pea.
Next day, upon the TV screen
a portly figure could be seen
appearing in unlikely spots
and interfering with the plots.
He's seen on adverts and the news,
consuming food and airing views.
He only just escaped alive
from clips of *Alien*, four and five
but found the travel programmes fun
with fancy food and lots of sun.
Now folks are flocking just to see
the favourite haunts of Percy Pea.
When, in a famous Shakespeare scene,
young Percy popped up on the screen,
'This is no dagger that I see,'
the actor cried, 'it's Percy Pea.'

53

The Queen, at Christmas, heaved a sigh
and muttered, 'Percy Pea and I . . .'
So, television fans, beware,
if, every night, you sit and stare
all glassy eyed before the box,
with clammy hands and sweaty socks,
when thunder rumbles just outside,
pull out your aerial, and hide.

Marian Swinger

Kenneth

who was too fond of bubble-gum and met an untimely end

The chief defect of Kenneth Plumb
Was chewing too much bubble-gum.
He chewed away with all his might,
Morning, evening, noon and night.
Even (oh, it makes you weep)
Blowing bubbles in his sleep.
He simply couldn't get enough!
His face was covered with the stuff.
As for his teeth — oh, what a sight!
It was a wonder he could bite.
His loving mother and his dad
Both remonstrated with the lad.
Ken repaid them for the trouble
By blowing yet another bubble.

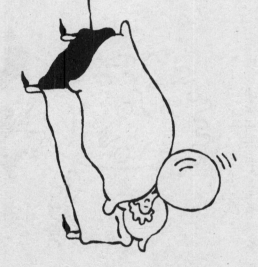

'Twas no joke. It isn't funny
Spending all your pocket money
On the day's supply of gum —
Sometimes Kenny felt quite glum.
As he grew, so did his need —
There seemed no limit to his greed:
At ten he often put away
Ninety-seven packs a day.

Then at last he went too far —
Sitting in his father's car,
Stuffing gum without a pause,
Found that he had jammed his jaws.
He nudged his dad and pointed to
The mouthful that he couldn't chew.
'Well, spit it out if you can't chew it!'
Ken shook his head. He couldn't do it.
Before long he began to groan —
The gum was solid as a stone.
Dad took him to a builder's yard;
They couldn't help. It was too hard.

solid

They called a doctor and he said,
'This silly boy will soon be dead.
His mouth's so full of bubble-gum
No nourishment can reach his tum.'

Remember Ken and please do not
Go buying too much you-know-what.

Wendy Cope

Once Too Often

The very first word from Jeremy Fry
Wasn't 'Mummy' or 'Daddy'
But the word 'Why?'
'Why should I finish my milk?
Tell me why!'

And as he grew older, Jeremy Fry
Drove everyone crazy
With his 'Why? Why? Why?'
'Why should I do as I'm told?
Tell me why!'

At school they despaired of Jeremy Fry
For in response to each answer
He'd always ask 'Why?'
'Why should I always believe what you say?
Tell me why!'

The end came so sudden for Jeremy Fry
When a pallet of bricks fell down from on high.
'Run!' shouted the workmen
To which he made reply
'Why should I do as you say?
Tell me . . .!'

So the very last word of Jeremy Fry
Wasn't 'Mummy' or 'Daddy',
Nor even 'Why?'
For he stopped once too often
To demand a reply.
'Why should I do as I'm told?
Tell me why!'

Alan Priestley

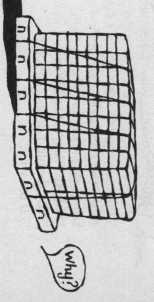

Only a Game

Wheeeee, pow, bang.
That's all they heard.
Dad said, 'These games are quite absurd.
Computer switched on all day long.
I don't care what you say, it's wrong.'
'Turn that off,' his mother screamed,
but still he sat and played and schemed,
slaughtering aliens as before,
gloating at the blood and gore,
destroying planets. In mid-zap
he heard a scratching, then a tap.
Outside the window, green and grim,
aliens had come for him.
'Oh brutal child,' their leader said,
'We've noticed how you want us dead.
We're going to take you for a trip.'
The mouse fell from his nerveless grip
as bug-eyed monsters swarmed inside.
'Save me, Mum and Dad,' he cried.
His parents heard a wham, zip, pow.
'Shut up,' they bellowed. 'Stop that row.'
The spaceship left. The empty room
echoed to its wheeeee, kaboom
which dwindled to a distant hum.
'That's better,' said his dad and mum.

Marian Swinger

Meryl Rose

Here's a tale of Meryl Rose
Who liked to push things up her nose . . .
    Lego, biscuits,
        Beads and bread —
            Rattled round inside her head.

A foolish girl — who wasted days
Playing with her silly craze —

Until upon a school photo day
She got the hamster out to play,
And with a grin and Meryl pout
She pushed poor Hammy up her snout!

'Look this way,' called photo man
'Smile or giggle if you can . . .'

Sweet Meryl posed
    with smile
        and pout —

And half a hamster hanging out!

Peter Dixon

When the Wind Changed

Sheree was always in disgrace
for when told off, she'd make a face
and drive her mum completely wild,
appearing more baboon than child,
or, sometimes like the Addams' Lurch
or else a gargoyle on a church.
Her mum, reproving her one day,
said, 'Your face will stay that way.
The wind will change and then, with luck
the face you're making will be stuck!'
Sheree just laughed, the little dunce,
and pulled another face at once.
Immediately (as you guessed)
the wind, then North, transferred to West.
Now all who see the child agree
she looks just like a chimpanzee.

Marian Swinger

ugh!

The Sad Story of Terrible Trevor

Terrible Trevor Alucard
Reckoned himself, he said, 'Well Hard'.
His favourite time was after dark.
He stalked the streets, he prowled the park.
'Where are you going?' his mum would shout
And Trev would always answer 'Out!'
At first, it seemed to him enough
To do the usual scary stuff,
Just walk about in studs and leather,
Chains and buckles and whatever,
But soon he found this rather boring
Like playing football without scoring.
'What can I do tomorrow night
To give everyone a proper fright?'
He asked himself, then scratched his head.
'The trouble with this town – it's dead!'
To tell the truth you'd seldom find
A fresh thought crossing Trevor's mind,
But suddenly he cried out, 'Hey,
The churchyard's got a right of way
Past all those crosses, angels' wings
And stones and spooky graves and things.
It's just the place to hang around,
To tiptoe up without a sound
And then with a blood-curdling cry
To leap out on any passers-by.'
So next day he spent his pocket-money
(All of it, every single penny)
On a cloak and fangs – vampire attire –
From *Van Helsing's Costume Hire*
And took it home. 'What's that you've got?
Asked Trevor's mum. 'I'll tell you what,
Mind your own business, woman!' Sad,

64

But Trev gave answers like his dad
And just like Dad he snarled and swore
Then stomped upstairs and slammed the door.

So night arrived and, fit to burst,
Trev was ready to do his worst.
I tell you, he could hardly wait
To dress up at the churchyard gate.
Once there he donned his vampire kit,
Just as he'd hoped, a perfect fit.
Now for a passer-by to scare.
As if the answer to a prayer
And much to Trevor's cruel delight
A hurrying figure came in sight.
At first it seemed to be the vicar
Except he was moving rather quicker,
Sort of floating down the path
With a sort of rather nasty laugh
(Crepuscular and melancholy)
Which Trev could tell was far from holy
Well before – oh send us grace! –
The two of them met up face to face
Like shadows looking in a mirror,
One with a grin, the other terror.
This was now way beyond a joke.
The grin flashed pointed fangs then spoke:
'My, what a silly boy you are,
Pretending to be Dracula
When everyone can see that you
Really haven't got a clue
About blood suction and all that.
You couldn't scare a witch's cat!
Your cloak's too short, your fangs are fake,
Your whole equipment's a mistake,
You should be drinking Seven-Up
Or bedtime cocoa from a cup

65

Instead of scaring little kids
With talk of garlic, coffin lids
And all the necks you're going to bite.
Still, Trev, since we've met tonight
We might as well become acquainted
(By this time Trev had nearly fainted!)
So shut your eyes and count to ten.
You won't have to pretend again.
Our meeting here is most fortuitous.
I need an apprentice, Trev, and you it is!
You've an awful lot to learn, I know,
But you're keen enough, it seems. Let's go,
Tomorrow is another day
And Transylvania's quite a way!'

With that, a flash and a clap of thunder
A cloak was swirled and Trev tucked under.
He might have given a muffled shout
But there was nobody else about
Except the cold dead, long engraved,
Indifferent to how a boy behaved
And, anyway, far too deep to hear
Or, if they did, too late to care.
Now, in the churchyard, one more stone
Under the yew tree all alone
Says Trevor Alucard RIP
Except he *doesn't*, believe you me!

John Mole

Why You Should Never Play on Roads

There was a boy called Lawrence Lowdes
Who liked to play on busy roads.

To make his pulse and heart rate quicken
He would play a game of chicken.

At the very last moment, out he'd race
Laughing in the driver's face.

He scampered out in front of bikes
Buses, scooters, vans and trikes.

Cars and lorries, four-wheeled drives
Like a cat with ninety lives.

Lawrence felt so bored one day
He thought he'd try a motorway.

Things moved there at greater speed
Giving Lol the thrill he'd need.

Soon his interest was caught
By a giant juggernaut.

Lawrence got himself prepared
And, waiting longer than he dared,

Out he ran, laughed and tripped
And in those massive tyres was gripped.

Round he whirled stuck to each wheel
But nobody could hear him squeal.

The moral is as clear as that
Little Lawrence was squashed flat.

So now across the nation's roads
Are lorry loads of Laurie Lowdes.

David Harmer

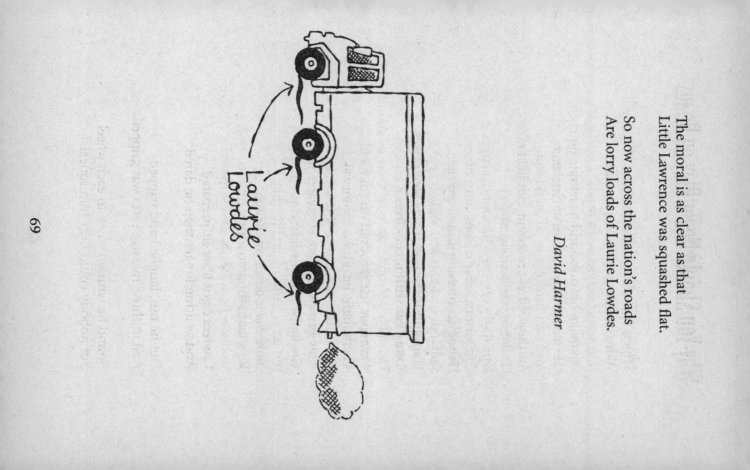

Laurie
Lowdes

Little Pete

This is the tale of little Pete
Who liked to put his size nine feet
Into wet concrete, or in mud,
In any place he found he could.
He liked to leave his footprints there,
And wait for folks to stop and stare
And say 'What are things coming to?
Or 'What a silly thing to do!'
One day – oh joy! – he found a street –
One vast expanse of wet concrete.
He took a running jump, and then
Sank out of sight; and sadly when
They found the boy, it was too late.
Young Pete had met an awful fate.
They chipped him out; now there he stands
With concrete gloves upon his hands,
A concrete coat, and concrete boots –
From head to toe, a concrete suit.
'How life-like!' strangers stop and say,
'You know it isn't every day
You see a work of art like that –
Look at the detail on his hat!'
But those who know stop on their way,
And bow their heads, and softly say
A prayer or two for little Pete,
Preserved forever in concrete.

Barbara Moore

70

Shrinking Violet

In school one morning, Violet Henn
Was chewing on her felt tip pen.
All of a sudden Violet found
She was much closer to the ground.
First she shrank to toddler size.
Her friends could not believe their eyes.
Next she shrank down even more,
To just six inches off the floor.
Meanwhile the teacher called for aid
From parents, police and fire brigade.
'Oh dear,' they cried. 'What *shall* we do?'
But, very sadly, no one knew.
By lunchtime, Violet was a dot
No bigger than a felt tip blot.
Then after lunch, she was so small
That she could not be seen at all.
At last, the teacher stood and sighed,
'Well, we have done our best. We tried.
Now we must learn from Violet Henn,
And *never* chew a felt tip pen.'

Sue Palmer and Michaela Morgan

Camouflage

Reggie Hawke just hated baths,
They seemed a waste of time,
And so he went from day to day
Completely caked in grime.

His mum would say, 'Now, Reggie dear,
You really ought to wash.'
But Reggie said, 'This hygiene thing
Is all a load of tosh.'

So day by day and week by week
Then month by month by year,
The grime got thicker all the time
With water nowhere near.

Eventually young Reg became
A solid, putrid heap –
The muck and filth and dirt and grime
Was now a metre deep.

And poppies, daisies, dandelions,
A little garden gnome,
Spiders, snails and slugs and worms
All made young Reg their home.

Beetles bedroomed in his ears,
And woodlice liked his nose,
His armpits housed a million ants
And spuds grew out his toes.

Alas, a sad and tragic end
Befell young Reggie Hawke —
He lay down for a little nap
While on a country walk.

He'd found the perfect resting stop —
A cosy unploughed field,
But that one little single snooze
Meant Reggie's fate was sealed.

For as he lay there fast asleep,
Why, who should then appear
But Farmer Fairfax on his plough —
The end was oh so near.

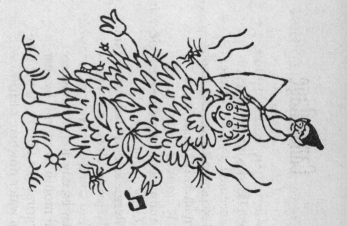

For Farmer Fairfax couldn't know
About the snoozing Reg –
After all, he looked just like
A pile of rotting veg.

And so he set about his work –
With jolly farmer's grin,
He cranked his tractor into gear
And ploughed poor Reggie in.

So readers, do take lots of care
When on a country walk –
You could be stepping on the bits
Of grubby Reggie Hawke.

Clive Webster

Isabella Deighton Down

Isabella Deighton Down
Caused a problem in her town.
For Isabella, strange of habit,
Believed she had been born a rabbit.

She twitched her nose and cocked an ear
And stuck a bobtail on her rear.
Then crouching down she bobbed around
Her bottom almost on the ground.

She didn't care where she ate lunch.
In any garden she would munch,
The vicar's carrots, dandelions
Or lettuces at Mrs Ryan's.

On traffic islands, so I'm told
She made a meal of marigold.
She dug her tunnels in the grass
And burrowed through the underpass.

When sent to school, she'd sit upright
And move her head from left to right
As rabbits do when they're alert
And pausing, on their patch of dirt.

When teacher spoke direct to her
She'd lift a leg to scratch her fur
Or thump her foot upon the floor
To warn of dangers that she saw.

At last her father in a rage
Thought she'd be better in a cage.
He was a most determined fella
So in the yard went Isabella.

Now you and I would rant and rave.
A cage would teach us to behave.
But Isabella thought it great
And settled happy, to her fate.

Till late one night when in her box
The all-pervading scent of fox
Made Isabella stiff with fright
(For rabbits are not brave in fight).

The cunning fox his jaws stretched wide
Found Isabella petrified.
Under the wire to reach his plunder,
The fox tore Isabel asunder.

The father wept to see his daughter
But knew the lesson he had taught her
Had served her right: Though still he cried
To think of how his daughter died.

Brenda Williams

Delilah Cleverclogs
(Who never knew when to shut up)

Delilah was an awful swot
Who always thought she knew the lot.
She didn't only *think* she knew,
She had to *tell* the whole world, too.

She sang her tables in the bath,
She shouted answers out in class,
Recited poems by the ton
And even spoke in French – for fun!

She chanted extracts from *The Times*
And well-known parts in pantomimes,
Repeated all the TV news
And football scores in shopping queues.

She really was a crashing bore.
'*We can't, we can't stand any more!*'
Her parents cried, and then devised
A plot to see Delilah off.

The dreaded pest they entered for
A quiz on space – moon, stars and all.
She answered every question right
And won First Prize (to their delight!)

They waved their hankies, jumped and cheered.
'*Help, help!*' she cried, and disappeared.
For a chattering swot what could be worse
Than a free trip round the Universe?

Patricia Leighton

Superheroes

Fearless poems chosen by Paul Cookson

SITUATION VACANT

COULD YOU BE
our next trainee Superhero/heroine?

Immediate vacancy exists for this challenging post
With excitement and adventure guaranteed uppermost.
Your duty will be to save the planet Earth
From an evil and imminent alien invasion.
Starting salary by negotiation.
Expected age range from twenty through to forty.
Applicants should be fit and keen and sporty.
Ability to fly (without wings) even better.
Apply now, by letter,
With full details and C.V.

To:-
Save the World plc.
P.O. Box 303
Gotham City
USA
(Closing date for applications is the 31st May)

Alan Priestley

Welcome to the Snake Hotel

Slithering poems chosen by Brian Moses

Dare you spend a night at The Snake Hotel?

There's an anaconda that likes to wander
    the corridors at night
and a boa that will lower itself onto guests
    as they search for the light.
And if, by chance, you lie awake
    and nearby something hisses,
I warn you now, you're about to be covered
    with tiny vipery kisses
    at the Ssssnake Hotel.

Brian Moses

Spill the Beans

An action-packed explosion of performance poems
by Paul Cookson and David Harmer

Meet Mr Moore the terrifying headmaster, join a picnic
on the M25, find out about the monster in the garden,
listen to the Tweaky Leaky Squeaky Brand New School
Shoe Blues, discover what lurks in a teacher's trouser
turn-ups, uncover some of the dinosaurs that time
forgot and much much more.

Mister Moore

Mister Moore, Mister Moore
Creaking down the corridor.

Uh uh eh uh
Uh uh eh uh

Mister Moore wears wooden suits
Mister Moore's got great big boots
Mister Moore's got hair like a brush
And Mister Moore doesn't like me much.

Mister Moore, Mister Moore
Creaking down the corridor.

Uh uh eh uh
Uh uh eh uh

Let Me Touch the Sky

Selected poems for Children by Valerie Bloom

Let Me Touch the Sky is a brand-new selection of Valerie
Bloom's warm, sparky and evocative poetry which will
delight readers of all ages.

Autumn Gilt

The late September sunshine
Lime green on the linden leaves
Burns bronze on the slated roof-tops,
Yellow on the farmer's last sheaves.

It flares flame-like on the fire hydrant,
Is ebony on the blackbird's wing,
Blue beryl on the face of the ocean,
Glints gold on the bride's wedding ring.

A sparkling rainbow on the stained-glass window,
It's a silver sheen on the kitchen sink,
The late September sunshine
Is a chameleon, I think.

A selected list of poetry books available from Macmillan

The prices shown below are correct at the time of going to press. However, Macmillan Publishers reserve the right to show new retail prices on covers which may differ from those previously advertised.

The Snake Hotel	0 330 48261 0	
Slithering poems, chosen by Brian Moses		£3.50
The Penguin in the Fridge	0 330 48019 7	
Poems by Peter Dixon		£3.50
Superheroes	0 330 48262 9	
Fearless poems, chosen by Paul Cookson		£2.99
Tongue Twisters and Tonsil Twizzlers	0 330 34941 4	
Poems chosen by Paul Cookson		£2.99
Let's Twist Again	0 330 37559 8	
More tongue twisters chosen by Paul Cookson		£2.99
A Sea Creature Ate My Teacher	0 330 39064 3	
Poems chosen by Brian Moses		£2.99
Never Stare at a Grizzly Bear	0 330 39121 6	
Poems by Nick Toczek		£2.99
Teachers' Pets	0 330 36868 0	
Poems chosen by Paul Cookson		£2.99

All Macmillan titles can be ordered at your local bookshop or are available by post from:

Book Service by Post
PO Box 29, Douglas, Isle of Man IM99 1BQ
Credit cards accepted. For details:
Telephone: 01624 675137
Fax: 01624 670923
E-mail: bookshop@enterprise.net
Free postage and packing in the UK.
Overseas customers: add £1 per book (paperback)
and £3 per book (hardback)